Tree-
House
Comix
Proudly
Presents

DOG MAN
LORD OF THE FLEAS

WRITTEN AND ILLUSTRATED BY **DAV PILKEY**

AS GEORGE BEARD AND HAROLD HUTCHINS

WITH COLOR BY JOSE GARIBALDI

graphix

AN IMPRINT OF

■SCHOLASTIC

THANK YOU TO A DEAR FRIEND, RACHEL "RAY RAY" COUN, WHO WAS THERE FROM THE START

Library of Congress Control Number 2017963497

978-0-545-93517-3 (POB)
978-1-338-29091-2 (Library)

10 9 8 7 6 5 4 3 2 1   18 19 20 21 22

Printed in China   62
First edition, September 2018

Edited by Anamika Bhatnagar
Book design by Dav Pilkey and Phil Falco
Color by Jose Garibaldi
Creative Director: David Saylor

CHAPTers

DOG MAN

BeHind the Epicness!

Yo, Homies, It's George and Harold again!

What up, dogs?

we're in 5th grade now, which means we're totally mature.

And deep!

I think I might grow a moustache!

me too!

SQUEAK SQUEAK SQUEAK

AWESOME!

But... our deepness and maturishness comes with a high Price tag.

Our new teacher makes us read **CLASSIC LITERATURE!**

Lord of the FLies
William Golding

Fortunately, the books have all been pretty good.

Don't you agree, Harold?

Well, um...

I didn't really finish <u>Lord</u> of the flies.

WHAT?

But don't worry! I've seen all the movies a bunch of times!!!

ALL **<u>WHAT</u>** movies?

You know: "**my Precious!**"

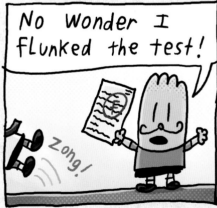

Well **I** read it, and it inspired me to write a new DOG man novel!

It's a story of savagery...

... a tale of consequences...

...A Profound Look into the constructs of morality...

... And one ring to rule them all!

SLAP!

But First, a recap of our story thus far...

OUR STORY THUS FAR...

by George and Harold

One time there was a cop and a police dog...

...Who got hurt in an explosion.

KA-BLAMMERS

When they got to the hospital, the doctor had sad news: Boo Hoo

I'm sorry, but your body is dying.

And your head is dying, too, cop!!!

Rats!!!

But just when everything seemed hopeless, the nurse Lady got an idea.

Let's sew the dog's head onto the cop's body!

OK, nurse Lady!

So they did.

And soon, a new crime-fighting sensation was unleashed.

HOORAY FOR DOG MAN!

Along the way, Dog Man has made some very awesome friends.

Zuzu: World's Greatest Poodle

Sarah Hatoff: world's Greatest reporter

Chief: world's Greatest chief

our Hero

And one supa evil enemy!

WANTED
for being a jerk

PETEY
world's most evilest cat

Recently, Petey tried to clone himself...

I'll make a big, evil villain, just like me!

...but instead, he got a tiny, cute Kitten who was <u>nothing</u> like him.

Papa!

Li'L Petey: world's Greatest kitty

Li'l Petey's Life started out sad...

Free Kitty

...but it wasn't sad for long.

Free kitty

DoG Man

Now Li'l Petey has a family.

Pat Pat Pat

Kiss Kiss Kiss

80-HD: world's Greatest Robot buddy

And that is a good place to start.

DoG Man

Tree-
House
coMix
Proudly
Presents

CHapTer 1

A visit from
Kitty
Protective
Services

DoG
Man

By George and Harold

One morning at Dog Man's house...

Buzz
Buzz
Buzz

clank
cLank
clank

DOG Man

...Li'l Petey and 80-HD were hard at work.

Buzz
Buzz
Buzz

clank
clank
clank

Well, I'm all done reprogramming the Dogmobile!

Now it's super easy to control!

How's the hydraulic Roof Ramp coming along?

CLAP CLAP

RRRR

RRR

RRRRRR

AWESOME!!!

CLUNK!

I can't wait until Dog Man sees it!

15

Grand Ballroom

♪Ding

Good morning, Dog Man!!!

Look what me and 80-HD did!

We transformed the Grand Ballroom into the coolest clubhouse **EVER**!!!

Us three are going to be in a club, ok?

We'll call ourselves the **SUPA BUDDIES!**

Most of the time, we'll just be our regular selves...

...But when danger rears its ugly head...

...We'll be super-heroes!!!

Look—I even made a cape for 80-HD!

And I made him a Flip-O-Rama mask!

... And 80-HD will be **Lightning Dude!**

Flop FLiP FLop FLiP

This is gonna be **sweeeeet!**

OH. It's time for Breakfast!

Cat food and cream for me...

...Dog food and gravy for you...

...And nuts and bolts and motor oil for 80-HD!

Grape nuts + Bolts

oiL

STEP 1.
First, place your left hand inside the dotted lines marked "Left hand here." Hold the book open FLAT!

STEP 2:
Grasp the right-hand page with your thumb and index finger (inside the dotted lines marked "Right Thumb Here").

STEP 3:
Now QUICKLY flip the right-hand page back and forth until the picture appears to be Animated.

(for extra fun, try adding your own sound-effects!)

O.RAMA

Remember,

while you are flipping,
be sure you can see
The image on page 23
AND the image on page 25.

If you flip quickly,
the two pictures will
start to look like
one **Animated** cartoon!

Don't forget to
add your own
sound-effects!

Left
hand here.

23

Right
Thumb
here.

That's **BETTER**!!!

DOG MAN

I was sent here by kitty Protective Services...

Apparently, you've got a kitten who should be in **School**!

Come with me, young man!

GRRRRRRRR

Don't You **DARE** Growl At **ME**!!!

I'll go to School...

...and **we** can play together when I get back, okay?

Bye, Dog Man! Bye, 80-HD!

Meanwhile...

Well, hello there, little fella.

Hi, Papa!

Ha-Ha! I think you've confused me with someone else!

No I haven't!

I'm a kindly old social worker!!!

No you're not.

I only care about your best interests!!!

No you don't.

Look, kid, I'm NOT who you THINK I Am!

Yes you are!

POP

PUNT

ZIP

Shuffle
Shuffle

NGYA!

Hey, where's the School at, Papa?

We're not going to School. We're getting outta town!

why?

Because you're in terrible **DANGER!**

why?

I'm not gonna tell you!

why?

Because every time I tell a Story, you always interrupt me, like, a Thousand Times!

why?

BECAUSE You're A PEST!!!

Why?

SiT DOWN!!!

why?

Because we need to talk!

why?

Look --- it's **very irritating** when you

Hey Papa, you got weird hairs in your nose!

You Just INTERRU

I won't interrupt anymore. I'll be good.

ALRight, because what I'm about to tell you is

Hey Papa, is this story gonna be boring?

NO!

Okay. You may continue.

Well, it all started this morning when I was in

Hey Papa! Do y'wanna hear a joke?

I AM GOING TO FINISH TELLING MY STORY...

...AND YOU ARE GOING TO LISTEN QUIETLY WITH NO INTERRUPTIONS!!!

Okay.

CHAPTER 2
PETEY'S STORY
(WiTH MANY (inTerrupTions))

ALRIGHT!
ALRIGHT!

I guess it all started when I was a kitten.

I used to be in the Critter Scouts!

Hey Papa, how come I'm wearing a hat?

That's NOT **You**! That's **ME** when I was a kitten!

Oh.

46

A flower!

A flower who?

A flower pooped on your head!

HA HA
HA HA
HA HA
HA HA
Ha Ha

Ha Ha
Ha Ha
Ha Ha
Ha Ha
HA
Ha

Petey did it!

Wait--- So that whole part about the Flood and the island was all make-believe?

Well, yeah--- but that's not the point!

The Point is, **I WAS BETRAYED!**

And then he started a **Fire!**

Then he fed my specs to the **SHARKS!**

We tried to **STOP** him!!!

JUST PAY ATTENTION!

Okay.

So Anyway...

...Then, we're gonna take over the world in our GIANT ROBO-BRONTOSAURUS!!!

It's Parked Outside!!!

HAW HAW HAW HAW HAW

HAW HAW HAW HAW HAW

So **THAT'S** why I came to get you...

...And **THAT'S** why we need to get as far away from here as possible.

But Papa, if the bad guys got locked up, why are we running?

Because they'll probably **ESCAPE!**

But how could they escape from a maximum security prison?

Who knows? Maybe something **DUMB** will happen!

Tree-House Comix Proudly Presents

Chapter 3

SomeThing DumB HAppens!

by George BeArd and HArold Hutchins

Meanwhile...

COPS

Ring-Ring

Hello?

chief

Help! There's been a JaiL escape!!!

chief

Where?

at the JaiL.

Oh!

chief

I'll put my best man on it!!!!!!!

chief

Oh, DOG MAN!

chief

69

70

Ten Minutes Later

Hello, I'm Sarah Hatoff reporting from Cat Jail...

...where chief and Milly have just caught three crooks!

How'd ya do it?

Well, first they attacked us...

Let's roll the clip...

...in Flip-O-Rama

Left hand here.

Right
Thumb
here.

Things were looking bad for us...

...So we ran to the Jail Library...

...and fought back using the **Power** of **BOOKS!**

Let's <u>B</u>ook These Bozos!

OK, roll the clip!

FLIP-O-RAMA

Left hand here.

Right
Thumb
here.

Well, congratulations on capturing the crooks!!!

Thanks. I only wish Dog Man was here.

Yeah, where **is** Dog Man?

I'm gonna find out!

Beep Beep Beep

RuFF RuFF RuFF

♪ RiNG-RiNG-RiNG ♫

DOG MAN--- wHeRe ARe YoU?

Come on, Zuzu! Let's follow them!

DOG MAN, Those Guys escaped because of YOU!!!

GO HOME!

But Chief—

Sorry, Milly, He's gotta Learn his Lesson!

...And WE'VE gotta catch those crooks Again!

Tree-
House
Comix
Proudly
Presents

CHAPTER 4
Revenge OF The FLEAS!

by George and Harold

Meanwhile...

Hey Papa! Knock-Knock!

WOULD YOU CUT THAT OUT?!!?

You're s'posed to say "Who's there?"

C'mon, Papa! It's a really awesome one this time!

Who's There?

Ummmm...

AAAAH!

Papa! You're s'posed to say "a big Robot brontosaurus who?"

This is Sarah Hatoff with a breaking news update!

A big Robot brontosaurus is attacking...

...and the good guys are in hot pursuit!

Now it's time for my exclusive interview with the crooks!!!

We're not crooks! We're megalomaniacs!

I am Piggy, Leader of the **FLEAS!!!**

The FLEAS?

It's an acronym for **F**uzzy **L**ittle **E**vil **A**nimal **S**quad!

But Boss, I'm not **F**uzzy.

And I'm not **L**ittle.

91

Left
hand here.

Right Thumb here.

A Ladder Pooped on your head.

Ha Ha Ha Ha Ha

A Ladder who?

Uhhh...

A Ladder.

That's not the point!

The point is, you were expecting someone named "Dwayne."

Cat Jail

But I switched it around!

That's why it's funny!

It woulda been funnier if the bathtub pooped on your head!

WHAT IS IT WITH YOU AND POOP?

Ha Ha Ha

...and expect to get a Laugh!

Ya gotta avoid repetition...

... Shun redundancy...

...eschew reiteration...

...resist recapitulation...

...And also, stop telling the same joke over and over!

CHAPTER 5

A Buncha Stuff That Happened Next

we now return with a breaking news update...

CLICK

LD

FWOOOSH!

SQUEEE!

FLOOOP!

FLIP FLOP FLIP FLOP FLIP FLOP FLIP FLOP FLIP FLOP FLIP FLOP FLIP FLOP

Meanwhile...

Where are we goin', Papa?

We've gotta get out of town! I told you!!!

No, Papa! We gotta go back and save Sarah and Zuzu and Milly and Chief!!!

We **CAN'T!** We don't have any weapons!

All we've got is this measly old Shrink ray! It only has **Two Shots** left!!!

But Papa—

Besides, I'm the **BAD GUY!** Everybody knows that!!!

But Papa—

I make poor decisions! I'm a **SCOUNDREL!!!**

But Papa—

I can't be goin' around being all **HEROIC** and stuff...

But Papa—

...I've got a **BAD REPUTATION** to uphold!!!

But Papa—

If you only knew the horrible things I've done...

...the awful, unforgivable things!!!

... Ummm... Atchoo Rebibyablabluh...

ALRight, ALRight! I Get the Point!!!

But if I help your friends, then **You've** gotta do something for **ME!**

What?

Hmmm...

What, Papa?

THAT'S IT!!!

You've gotta stop calling me "Papa."

but why?

Look — we've been through this a MILLION TIMES!

I AM NOT YOUR PAPA!

You're MY CLONE! There's A BIG DIFFERENCE!!!

okay.

Okay **What**?

Okay, Petey.

That's **BETTER!**

Now Let's go save those silly friends of Yours!!!

ahhh...

a cloud...

A cloud, who?

A cloud pooped on your nose!

Ha Ha Ha Ha Ha Ha Ha Ha

Oops. I mean, Hi, The Bark Knight!

Hi, 80-HD!

HEY!

I mean, Hi, Lightning Dude!!!

CRASH

You guys look awesome in your costumes!

I sure wish I hadn't forgotten **Mine!**

CHAPTER 6

SUPA BUDDIES

134

DON'T WAVE AT HIM! HE'S OUR ENEMY!

And any enemy of **OURS** shall soon be **ANNIHILATED!**

What do you have to say to **THAT?**

Knock-Knock!

THAT'S **NOT** FUNNY!!!

Hey, The Bark Knight...

...now's our chance to save our friends!!!

Ready?

GO!

SWOOSH

shinG shinG

SLice

chief

chief

WE'RE FALLING!

Well, when you think about it...

None of us existed for trillions of years **BEFORE** we were born...

..And we didn't seem to mind it then!

Yeah--- I didn't even notice!!!!

True dat!

Let's not cry 'cuz we're Gonna die. Let's Laugh 'cuz we Got to **LiVE!!!**

Ha-Ha!

Yeah! Ha-Ha!

FACTORY

Don't celebrate just yet...

... 'CUZ we're **BAAAAACK!!!**

It took forever, but we finally got ourselves out from under that building!!!

And **NOW**, we're gonna finish you **ALL** off...

...with **ONE ZAP** of our **killer death ray!**

So you'd better say "Goodbye!"

Bye-bye, Dog Man!

So Long, Sarah!

chief

Au revoir, Zuzu!

Adiós, Milly!

We love you, 80-HD!

WOULD YOU GUYS STOP BEING SO PLEASANT ABOUT EVERYTHING?!?

GO ON, ZAP 'em!

ZAP

Looks Like we're gonna have a Giant Robo-Battle...

...iN FLiP-O-RAMA!

Left hand here.

153

Right
Thumb
here.

I don't know **why** you're helping those guys...

YOU'RE A VILLAIN!

Yeah, I know—but...

...but I'm tryin' to change.

OH, REeeeALLY? Well How's **THiS** For a change?

FLiP-O-RAMA

Left hand here.

Right
Thumb
here.

Left hand here.

Right
Thumb
here.

That's my Papa!

I mean, that's Petey!

He's trying so hard to be good!

I always knew he had a good heart in there somewhere!

CHAPTER 7
The Darkness

Two hours Later...

PETEY!!!

CLONK

We've been battling for **HOURS**...

...And it hasn't gotten us **ANYWHERE!!!**

So I was thinking...

...why are we fighting amongst **ourselves?**

If you and I set aside our differences...

...and we worked **TOGETHER...**

We'd be **UNSTOPPABLE!**

I mean, *REALLY*...

Haven't you always wanted a sidekick?

A Partner in crime?

Isn't that why you Created that dumb Little kitten in the first place?

Li'L Petey—
What a Wimp!

Hi—I'm Li'L Petey!
Ooh—I'm so cute
and little and
ever so **GOOD!!!**

HAW HAW HAW
HAW HAW
HAW

You can
change, Papa.

Ya just gotta
switch expectations!

So what do ya say, old buddy?

Let's ditch that obnoxious kid and go do some **Crimes!**

Don't TALK About MY Son That WAY!

Your **S<u>O</u>N?**

I thought he was your **cLone!**

Yeah, my **cLone!** That's — that's what I meant.

Meanwhile...

Everyone was Transfixed by the drama above...

... When Suddenly...

AWESOME!

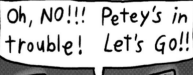

Oh, NO!!! Petey's in trouble! Let's Go!!

Well, well, well...

All of my **Enemies** Are together in **ONE PLACE!** How **CONVENIENT!!!**

OH, **CRUNKY!** OH, **BUB!!!**

CRUNKY! BUB!!!

I-I can't believe you guys saved me!

We're the good guys, Petey!

That's what we do!

But...

...Where's the kid?

WHERE'S Li'L PETEY?

I'm up here, playin' with the bad guys!

80-HD!!!

We gotta save Dog Man!!!

Oops! I mean, **Lightning Dude!!!**

We gotta save **The Bark Knight!!!**

DOG MAN--- WAKE UP!!!

The Bad guys Are Coming!!!

Well, well, well... What do we have here?

It Looks like you guys got yourselves in a big **Mess!!!**

Do you have any **LAST Words** before we **ZAP** you all to **SMiThereens?**

Ummm...

...hmmm...

192

We'll tell ya our last word in a minute, ok?

MR. SQUiRTY'S SPRAY PAiNT FACTORY

Red Paint

Green Paint

Excuse me, Mr. Squirty, may I have this?

OK, Strange flying Cyborg kitten I've never met before. Take whatever you like!

Thanks, Mister Squirty!

ZOOM

Quadruple FLIP-O-Rama

Left hand here.

Right
Thumb
here.

Love, Sloppily

Right Thumb here.

Love, Sloppily

Hey Papa, Look!

Dog Man Kissed us!

Yeeeeeeeeah...

...Lovely.

HOORAY FOR DOG MAN! ...OOPS, WE MEAN The BARK Knight!

CHAPTER 8

MY DOG MAN HAS FLEAS!

Well, I guess we— hey, what's that?

What is it, Papa?

It's that Shrink ray I dropped back in chapter five.

Oh, yeah!

I wonder if it still works.

Let's find out!!!

ZAP

Yep. It worked!

Sweeeet!

Hey Gang! Petey saved the day!!!

HOORAY FOR PETEY!!!

They're **GONE!**

NOW LOOK WHAT YOU'VE DONE!!!

THE BAD GUYS GOT AWAY AGAIN!

216

But I'm a good guy now!!!

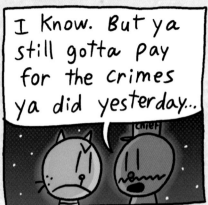

I know. But ya still gotta pay for the crimes ya did yesterday...

...and the day before that, and the day before that, and the...

Well THAT'S JUST GREAT!!!

I WAS GOOD FOR, LIKE, THE WHOLE BOOK!

AND iT DiDN'T MAKE ANY DifFerence!

Dog Man, I'm gonna go with them, okay?

Don't worry. Chief will walk me home.

scratch scratch scratch

G'night everybody! Let's all play again tomorrow!!!

If you're happy, People just get **JeALOUS!**

Ya gotta be happy anyway, Papa!

You can spend **YEARS** creating Stuff...

...Then a big robot brontosaurus can come along...

... and **ZAP** it all To **SMITHEREENS** in **TWO SECONDS!!**

Ya gotta be creative anyway, Papa.

PETEY-You're BACK!

KA-CLICK

Hey kid, Y'wanna get some gelato with me after I escape tomorrow?

I don't Know what gelato is, but okay!

Well, So Long, Petey!

G'night, Chief!

Hey Chief, what's gelato?

It's like ice cream.

Oh.

sweeeet!

BUT WAiT...

...if you thought our adventure was over...

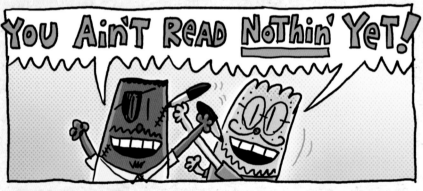

YOU AiN'T READ NOThiN' YET!

Right now, George and Harold are busy reading **ANOTher** old-fashioned book...

The Call OF The WILD Jack London

The Call of The WILD Jack London

...getting **AWESOME New-FASHioned ideas**...

... and desperately trying to figure out how to remove permanent marker from their faces before their moms find out!

So get ready for the next epic tale...

... of maturishness and deepality!!!

Because an all-new DOG MAN novel is coming!!!

Tree-House CoMix Proudly Presents

DOG MAN
BRAWL of the WILD

If You Like **THRILLS**...

...and you like **LAFFS**...

...and You Like **AWESOMENESS**...

...Then DOG MAN is GO!

"Dog Man is Go?"

That don't make no Sense!

BUT WE LIKE it!!!

230

CAT KID

234

LIGHTNING DUDE LD

PiGGY

in **33** Ridiculously easy steps!

NOTES

by George and Harold

★ Our favorite character from William Golding's <u>Lord of the Flies</u> is Piggy. The Piggy in our book is a bad guy, though.

★ The dialogue on page 147 was inspired by quotes commonly attributed to Mark Twain and Dr. Seuss.

★ The conversation on pages 220-221 was inspired by the poem "Anyway," by Kent M. Keith. A version of this poem is inscribed on the wall of Mother Teresa's home for children in Calcutta, India.

★ "I finally finished reading <u>Lord of the Flies</u>. It was awesome." —Harold Hutchins

ReAd to Your CAT, Kid!

* University of California-Davis: Reading to Rover, 2010

THATS FAKE NEWS!!!

it is?

Well, no — Probably not...

...but it's only **HALF** of the story!!

Experts believe that Kids can Get the **SAME BENEFITS**...

...by reading out Loud to **CATS!!!**

really?

BUT There's MORE!

Because **NOW,** There's a **NEW READING CRAZE** That's All the **RAGE!!!**

It's happening at animal shelters Everywhere!!!

ANIMAL SHELTER

Kids * can show up and reAd to Shelter cats!!!

The Kids get all of the great benefits from reading out loud to cats...

* accompanied by a parent or guardian

... and the cats get the benefits of human interaction and socialization.

This helps make it easier for shelter cats to get adopted!

It's a **Win-Win** for everybody!

Wow! That's a great idea, Papa!

CLICK

2 hours Later...

Cat Jail

Hey Petey! You've got a visitor!!!

I do?

Hey Kid. What'cha doing here?

I came to read to my cat, kid!

Really?

check with
your local
animal shelter
and see if you
can volunteer to
**Read To Your
Cat, Kid!**

READING TO YOUR CAT IS ALWAYS A PAWS-ITIVE EXPERIENCE!

SOPHIE & SKIPPY

MAUDE & MAX

MAUDE & ABBY

MAX & ALEX

CHARLIE & PAPOOSA

#ReadToYourCatKid

AARON & PAPOOSA

JAC, KATE & DELILAH

KOUME, RINKA & YUMA

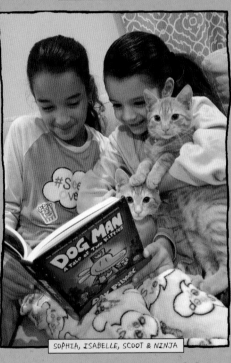

SOPHIA, ISABELLE, SCOOT & NINJA

GALEN, FINN & RUCKUS

**LEARN MORE AT
PILKEY.COM!**

ABOUT THE AUTHOR-ILLUSTRATOR

When Dav Pilkey was a kid, he suffered from ADHD, dyslexia, and behavioral problems. Dav was so disruptive in class that his teachers made him sit out in the hall every day. Luckily, Dav loved to draw and make up stories. He spent his time in the hallway creating his own original comic books.

In the second grade, Dav Pilkey created a comic book about a superhero named Captain Underpants. His teacher ripped it up and told him he couldn't spend the rest of his life making silly books.

Fortunately, Dav was not a very good listener.

ABOUT THE COLORIST

Jose Garibaldi grew up on the South Side of Chicago. As a kid, he was a daydreamer and a doodler, and now it's his full-time job to do both. Jose is a professional illustrator, painter, and cartoonist who has created work for Dark Horse Comics, Disney, Nickelodeon, MAD Magazine, and many more. He lives in Los Angeles, California, with his wife and their cats.